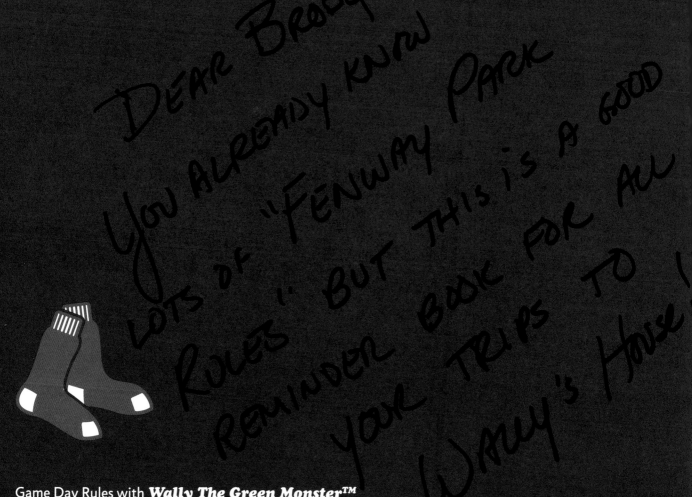

Dear Brody
You already know
Lots of "Fenway Park
Rules", But this is a good
Reminder book for all
your trips to
Wally's House!

Love,
Dady + Dady

Spring 2014

Game Day Rules with **Wally The Green Monster**™

Story © 2013 by Sherri Graves Smith

Requests for permission to make copies of any part of the work should be submitted online at info@mascotbooks.com or mailed to Mascot Books, 560 Herndon Parkway #120, Herndon, VA 20170.

Major League Baseball trademarks and copyrights are used with permission of Major League Baseball Properties, Inc. Visit MLB.com

PRT1113A

Printed in the United States

ISBN-13: 9781620864142
ISBN-10: 1620864142

www.mascotbooks.com

GAME DAY RULES
with
WALLY
THE GREEN MONSTER™

BOSTON RED SOX™

Sherri Graves Smith
Illustrated by Preston Asevedo

Hello, I'm *Wally The Green Monster* and welcome to *Fenway Park*, home of the *Boston Red Sox*. As you already know, the *Red Sox* are the greatest team in all of the land.

I'm here to teach you how to show your *Red Sox* pride in a special way,
by following these simple rules on our big game day!

When you're standing in a line,
it is best to take your time.

Patience is something you will learn,
when you kindly wait your turn.

It is polite to greet those you meet with a friendly "hi" or "hello."
But don't go to strangers alone. Try it first with someone you know!

It can be very crowded in the stands.
Please be careful and hold your parent's hand.

If you step on someone's feet,
on the way to your seat,

"excuse me" or "I'm sorry" will do
when asking someone to pardon you.

Remember it is thoughtful to say,
"you're forgiven" or "that's okay."

Before the National Anthem starts,
take caps off heads and put hands on hearts.

If you need help or a special favor,
use the word "please" with your friend or neighbor.

If you help someone, and they say "thanks" to you,
just say "you're welcome." It's the right thing to do.

Remember, it is nice to share with others,
not just your sisters or brothers.

If someone does something kind,
a simple thank you will do just fine.

If a player makes a mistake,
it's never a reason to act with hate.

When a play goes very well,
it's good to say the player's swell.

It is great to love our team,
but to our rivals, don't be mean.

It is okay to jump around,
just do not knock someone down.

It is even okay to catch the ball, just do
not snatch it or make someone fall!

It is fine to celebrate and cheer with fans,
just be close to your parents in the stands.

It is great to sing and sway.
After all, it's about having fun on this game day.

If the ump's call is not for us,
it's not right to shout and fuss.

If the ump's call puts us in first place,
let's not rub it in our opponent's face.

Even though players get their job done
by keeping the other team from scoring runs,
be sure to watch them interact carefully.
Players help each other and try not to bully.

If the other team does win,
remember you will play again!

If our team comes out on top,
it is great to cheer a lot!
But a sore winner, you should never be.
Winning is not a reason to be mean.

Remember before you leave the game,
clean the spot from where you came.

If you're five or seventeen
you can always help someone in need.

If you want to see good sportsmanship and have some time to wait,
at the end of the game look downfield to watch the teams congratulate.

Thank you for taking the time
to read the manners in this rhyme.

When we mind our manners watch and see,
how much better sports can be!

Now, my *Red Sox* friend, I am so glad that we were able to meet!
Come back to *Fenway* soon, and I'll be right here at the lone red seat!

Check out these other *Game Day* titles from Sherri Graves Smith and Mascot Books:

-***New York Yankees*** *Game Day Rules* (New York)

-*Albert and Alberta's Game Day Rules* (Florida)

-*Big Al's Game Day Rules* (Alabama)

-*Mike the Tiger's Game Day Rules* (LSU)

-*Buzz's Game Day Rules* (Georgia Tech)

-*Cimarron's Game Day Rules* (Florida State)

-*Hairy Dawg's Game Day Rules* (Georgia)

-*Rameses' Game Day Rules* (North Carolina)

-*Aubie's Game Day Rules* (Auburn)

-*Smokey's Game Day Rules* (Tennessee)

-*Cocky's Game Day Rules* (South Carolina)

-*Tiger's Game Day Rules* (Clemson)

-*Reveille's Game Day Rules* (Texas A&M)

-*Bully's Game Day Rules* (Mississippi State)

-*Nittany Lion's Game Day Rules* (Penn State)

More to come!

Visit www.GameDayRules.com

for more information.

A Note from the Author

Photo © Sara Hanna Photography - www.SaraHanna.com. The photo was taken at the Swan Coach House.

Sports are more than just a form of exciting entertainment or even a great way to exercise. Sports are a fantastic way to build self-esteem and bring together a sense of community that crosses gender, race, age, economic, social, and even religious lines.

There are many important life lessons that can be learned through sports – how to win AND to lose with grace, being a team player, learning from mistakes, civility towards opposing teams, playing by the rules, respecting the decisions made by the officials – to just name a few. Those skills can be translated into the classroom, the board room, and even in handling the everyday ups and downs of life.

In writing this pledge, it is my goal to instill the solid values of competing with respect, dignity, and integrity in our children, our nation's greatest asset.

-Sherri

SPORTSMANSHIP
PLEDGE

LEARN

I will learn how to play the sport, like running and catching the ball.
Learning how to play is great, but having fun is best of all!

EXCELLENCE

I will strive for excellence and live to the best of my best potential.
Doing the best you can is always an essential!

GROWTH

I will exercise my body and the brain in my head.
It is important that they are healthy and that I keep them both well-fed!

INTEGRITY

I will be respectful, honest, and fair, and play according to the rules.
I will behave this way whether at play, at home, or at school!

TEAMWORK

Each member of the team is important, whether coach, player, or me.
I will support them and do my part so we can be the best that we can be!

PLEDGE OF SUPPORT
The Sportsmanship Pledge is an important foundation upon which I will foster and build.
I will be an example and show leadership in this pledge whether on or off the field!

Have a book idea?

Contact us at:

Mascot Books
560 Herndon Parkway
Suite 120
Herndon, VA 20170

info@mascotbooks.com | www.mascotbooks.com